The Spaceship

First published in 2010
by Wayland

Text copyright © Cynthia Rider
Illustration copyright © Sandra Aguilar

Wayland
338 Euston Road
London NW1 3BH

Wayland Australia
Level 17/207 Kent Street
Sydney, NSW 2000

Series Editor: Louise John
Cover design: Paul Cherrill
Design: D.R.ink
Consultant: Shirley Bickler

A CIP catalogue record for this book is available from the British Library.

ISBN 9780750261166

Printed in China

Wayland is a division of Hachette Children's Books,
an Hachette UK Company

www.hachette.co.uk

The Spaceship

Written by Cynthia Rider
Illustrated by Sandra Aguilar

WAYLAND

"Let's play with our space toys," said Molly.

"Let's make a spaceship
for them," said Zac.

Zac made a
silver spaceship.

He stuck some gold
stars on it.

Molly made a blue top
for the spaceship. Zac
put it on.

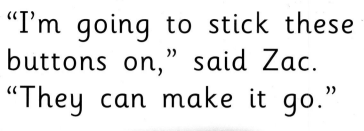

"I'm going to stick these buttons on," said Zac. "They can make it go."

"Look at this red and yellow paper," said Molly. "We can put it on the spaceship."

"I'm going to call our spaceship Zoom," said Zac.

"Spaceship Zoom is ready to go," shouted Zac. "3... 2... 1... Blast off!"

"Look out!" shouted Molly.
"The aliens are going to
get the spaceship."

"Zoom! Zoom! Zoom!"
shouted Zac.

Just then, Dad came in.

"Look out!" said Zac. "Here comes a real alien!"

"Come on! Let's get the alien," shouted Molly.

START READING is a series of highly enjoyable books for beginner readers. **The books have been carefully graded to match the Book Bands widely used in schools.** This enables readers to be sure they choose books that match their own reading ability.

Look out for the Band colour on the book in our Start Reading logo.

The Bands are:

Pink Band 1A & 1B

Red Band 2

Yellow Band 3

Blue Band 4

Green Band 5

Orange Band 6

Turquoise Band 7

Purple Band 8

Gold Band 9

START READING books can be read independently or shared with an adult. They promote the enjoyment of reading through satisfying stories supported by fun illustrations.

Cynthia Rider lives in the Peak District of Derbyshire and often finds inspiration for her stories in the countryside around her. She particularly enjoys writing for young children and encouraging their love of reading.

Sandra Aguillar enjoys the challenge of creating new characters and making them smile, shout or moan, which is why she decided to become an illustrator! If she had to draw herself her eyes would be huge and round and her smile would go from ear to ear.